By You
For You

Project Be is about you.

These pages are meant to encourage you to reflect,

reconnect with yourself and others, find joy, take action.

Be who you are.

Create a life that you will love.

Published in the United States of America.
Library of Congress Cataloging-in-Publication Data is available.

ISBN-13: 978-0-9908233-0-8

Written by Wanda Chaves and Jennifer Chaves
Art and Design by Sadie Stetson

Additional Collaborators: Helen Krol and Heriberto Chaves

Printed in the United States of America.
First printing October 2014

FOR MAMI
THANK YOU FOR GIVING US THE WORLD

PARA PAPI
GRACIAS POR QUERERNOS TANTO SIEMPRE

TO STEVE HICKNER
YOU ARE ONE OF THE MOST COLORFUL PEOPLE
THAT WE KNOW

AND

TO THE ZUNIS
THE NINE OF YOU INSPIRE MY LIFE WITH YOUR
INCREDIBLE SPIRIT AND LIGHT

who in the world am I?
Ah, that's the greatest puzzle.
            - Lewis Carroll, Alice in Wonderland

your visions will become clear only
when you can look into your own heart.
who looks outside, dreams.
who looks inside, awakes.

                        - C.G. Jung

It's not about
WHAT DO I WANT TO BE (when I grow up)
but about
WHO DO I WANT TO BE
and
WHO I ALREADY AM.

Project Be

BE FIRST. THEN WHAT.

Project Be is about you.
You are the most important project that you will ever undertake.

The next time you walk into a room full of people, or
are in the middle of a crowd, look around. Most people
in the world look like black and white characters in a
film. They blend into their environments and into each
other. They are living their lives unquestioning, on
automatic pilot. They are unsure of who they are and
unclear about the life they want to create for themselves.

Among the crowds of black and white characters, walk
individuals who have a radiant color about them and a
brilliant light shining inside. Their energy is powerful
and at the same time peaceful. You immediately feel it
when you meet them. Instead of going through life asleep,
they have chosen to live wide-awake. They are
comfortable in their own skin, are connected to their core,
and feel passionate about their lives. They do not follow
the crowd and stay true to who they are. They listen to
their intuition and it guides them.

In a black and white world, they choose to live in color.
You too have the power to choose.

Instead of stressing about what you want to be (when you
grow up), take the time to discover who you already are.
Give yourself the permission to be completely yourself,
and this will give you courage and freedom. Ask
yourself the questions that are important to you and
commit to undertaking the continuous journey of self-
discovery. Believe in your dreams and take action.
Seek possibilities that excite you and plant seeds to see
what may grow. This will lead you to the adventures
and paths that you will travel to continuously be
creating your beautiful, authentic life.

The path to color may not always be an easy one and you may sometimes feel lost. But if you stay committed to your journey and continue to explore, your light will shine brighter, more colors will enter into your life and make you stand out in the black and white world of those who choose to live their lives wide asleep.

Take the pledge below to commit to Be.

My Pledge to Be Me:
Even if it is painful and tiring and uncomfortable at times, I want to dig deep. I do not want the countless distractions that surround me to consume me nor take me away from my journey. I will not allow these distractions to disconnect me from my true self, from others, from the natural world of which I am a part, and from achieving my dreams. I will listen with my heart. Peel the layers. Cultivate self-awareness. Have courage when I struggle. Focus. Seek light, color, and joy. Be wide-awake.

I am and will choose to Be Me.

Sign your name here:

Fill this journal and your life with questions, thoughts, authentic feelings, and bright colors.

I CHOOSE TO BE IN FULL
COLOR AND TO LIVE MY
LIFE WIDE-AWAKE.

BEGIN YOUR JOURNEY HERE

find a quiet comfortable place...

sit

outside

or in a special
corner of your home

under a
tree

relax

and write

draw

doodle

just be.

MY NAME iS Bri

iAM a sister and daughter

iAM nuturing

iAM caring

iAM loving

iAM motivated

iAM Type-A

iAM me

I ALSO WANT TO BE...

a journalist for Alternative Press

I want to write Profile stories
and Q:A stories

I want to conduct research
on infertility

I want to make a ~~difference~~
difference

I want to do things CORRECT

A — LETTER OF THE ALPHABET

Lane from Alice in Chains — SINGER

Saturn — PLANET

— CHARACTER

Willow — TYPE OF TREE

Triple chocolate Snickers — FLAVOR OF ICE CREAM

— MEMORY

my life perfectly planned out — DAYDREAM

Operation — GAME I PLAYED AS A KID

Finch — BIRD

JUST FOR FUN
MY FAVORITE... my sister — PERSON (ALIVE OR DEAD)

TOY

WORD "Cunt"

PART OF MY BODY Eyes

POEM "Daddy" by Slyvia Plath

SUPER HERO Captain America

BOOK Too many
GOT

TIME OF DAY Night time

QUOTE Fuck off

BODY OF WATER Atlantic

LYRICS

How Would I DESCRIBE MYSELF?

WHAT MAKES ME
UNIQUELY ME?

WHAT ARE MY

Good Habits

WHAT ARE MY

Bad
Habits

WHAT ARE MY
SKILLS?

CIRCLE YOUR STRONGEST SKILLS

WHAT ARE MY
CHARACTERISTICS?

CIRCLE YOUR STRONGEST CHARACTERISTICS

A CHANGE THAT I WANT TO MAKE IN MYSELF OR MY LIFE IS...

SPEND SOME TIME LOOKING AROUND
YOUR LIVING SPACE
(ROOM, HOUSE, APARTMENT, GARDEN)
IN YOUR CLOSET,
AT YOUR CLOTHES...

WHAT DO MY LIVING SPACE AND BELONGINGS SAY ABOUT ME?

Fill this page with thoughts and images

that have been on your mind lately

WHERE AM i IN

MENTALLY
SPIRITUALLY

MY LIFE RIGHT NOW?

PHYSICALLY

EMOTIONALLY

THE LAST TIME I

Laughed

WAS...

THE LAST TIME I CRIED

OPEN A DRAWER IN YOUR DRESSER
OR DESK.
CLEAN IT OUT.

MAKE TWO PILES:
THINGS TO KEEP
THINGS TO GIVE AWAY

WHAT DO THE THINGS I WANT TO KEEP MEAN TO ME?

WHAT DO THE THINGS THAT I WANT TO GIVE AWAY OR
THROW OUT SAY ABOUT ME?

How do i
honestly feel
about myself
and my life
today?

GO BACK TO YOUR LIST OF GOOD AND
BAD HABITS...
PICK ONE OF YOUR BAD HABITS AND

Break

HOW WOULD OTHERS DESCRIBE ME?

MY...
PARENTS
BEST FRIEND
ACQUAINTANCES
BROTHER/SISTER
PARTNER

MY...
BOSS
TEACHER
NEIGHBOR
GRANDMOTHER
OTHER IMPORTANT PEOPLE IN MY LIFE

ASK SOMEONE WHO KNOWS
YOU WELL TO DESCRIBE YOU

ASK SOMEONE WHO YOU JUST
RECENTLY MET TO DESCRIBE YOU

[WRITE WHAT THEY SAID HERE]

I DAYDREAM
ABOUT...

WHAT DO I LOVE?

WHY DO I LOVE
THESE PEOPLE, EXPERIENCES,
THINGS?

LIST

AT LEAST 20 PEOPLE,
OBJECTS,
EXPERIENCES THAT YOU LOVE.

WHAT DOES MY LOVE AND
PASSION
FOR THEM SAY ABOUT ME?

PUT AN IMAGE OF
SOMETHING
YOU LOVE
ON YOUR WALL

HOW AM I CREATIVE IN MY EVERYDAY LIFE?

WHAT DOES BEING CREATIVE MEAN TO ME?

I FEEL MOST
CREATIVE WHEN...

I FEEL ENERGIZED
AND EXCITED
WHEN...

TAKE SOME TIME FOR YOURSELF TODAY
DO SOMETHING THAT MAKES YOU VERY HAPPY

WHAT DRAINS MY ENERGY?

WHAT DO I DISLIKE?
BE SPECIFIC.

WHY DO I DISLIKE
THESE TASKS,
PEOPLE, THINGS,
RESPONSIBILITIES?

WHO DO I DISLIKE?

WHAT DOES MY DISLIKE OF THEM SAY ABOUT ME?

CUT SOMETHING OUT OF YOUR LIFE
TODAY THAT DRAINS YOUR ENERGY

WHEN HAVE I FELT *happiest* IN MY LIFE?

WHEN HAVE I FELT MOST SAD OR MISERABLE?

write, draw, paint, doodle...
Fill this page in whatever
way moves you

AM I TAKING CARE OF MYSELF,
OF MY HEALTH AND WELL-BEING?
DO I...

SLEEP ENOUGH?

EAT FOODS
THAT NOURISH
MY BODY?

MAKE TIME
FOR MYSELF?

WHAT DO I NEED?

daily commitment

CHOOSE AN ACTION THAT YOU WILL
DO FOR YOURSELF EVERYDAY.
COMMIT TO DOING THAT ACTION
EVERY DAY FOR THE NEXT 30 DAYS

EXAMPLES OF DAILY ACTIONS FOR YOURSELF: TAKE A 30-MINUTE WALK. SIT IN SILENCE FOR 15 MINUTES. DANCE OR DO YOGA FOR 20 MINUTES. WRITE THREE PAGES IN YOUR JOURNAL. DRAW SOMETHING. PLANT A SEED. DRINK SEVEN GLASSES OF WATER. TAKE A NAP. EAT SOMETHING HEALTHY EVERY DAY. CLEAN AND DE-CLUTTER A PART OF YOUR SPACE FOR 30 MINUTES. SING OR LISTEN TO A SONG THAT MAKES YOU VERY HAPPY.

WHEN WAS THE LAST TIME I FELT ANGRY?

WHY DID I FEEL ANGRY?

WHAT DOES THIS
ANGER SAY ABOUT
ME AND WHAT IS
IMPORTANT TO ME?

I feel most relaxed and
happy when...

How often do I feel relaxed and happy?
What and who make me happy?

WHEN DO I FEEL MOST STRESSED AND TIRED? HOW OFTEN DO I FEEL STRESSED AND TIRED?

WHAT IS CAUSING MY STRESS AND TIREDNESS?

WHAT IS MY RELATIONSHIP WITH THE NATURAL WORLD AROUND ME?

AND WITH THE LIVING BEINGS WITH WHOM I SHARE THIS PLANET?

WHAT DO I WANT THIS RELATIONSHIP TO BE?

SPEND SOME TIME OUTSIDE TODAY. GO FOR A WALK, SIT QUIETLY AND LISTEN.

WHO ARE MY ROLE MODELS?
WHY DO I LOOK UP TO THEM?

AM I MAKING AN IMPACT ON THE LIVES OF OTHERS? HOW?

DO I WANT TO MAKE AN IMPACT? ON WHOM? HOW?

ASK SOMEONE
YOU KNOW
TO DESCRIBE
HOW YOU
IMPACT OTHERS

on this page

EXPLORE SOMETHING

that is important to you

CONTACT SOMEONE
YOU LOOK UP TO
AND HAVE ALWAYS
WANTED TO MEET.
INVITE HIM/HER TO
GO FOR TEA OR
COFFEE WITH YOU.

what have been the most important moments

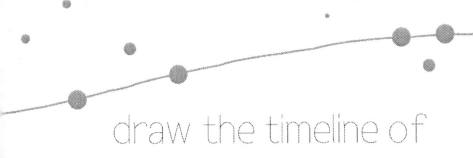

draw the timeline of

and turning points
in my life?

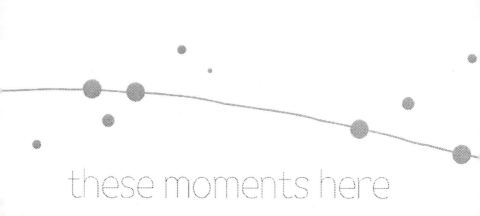

these moments here

THE MOST IMPORTANT
MOMENTS OF MY LIFE:

WHAT I LEARNED
ABOUT MYSELF FROM
THIS MOMENT:

WHAT/WHO ARE THE...
4 EVENTS

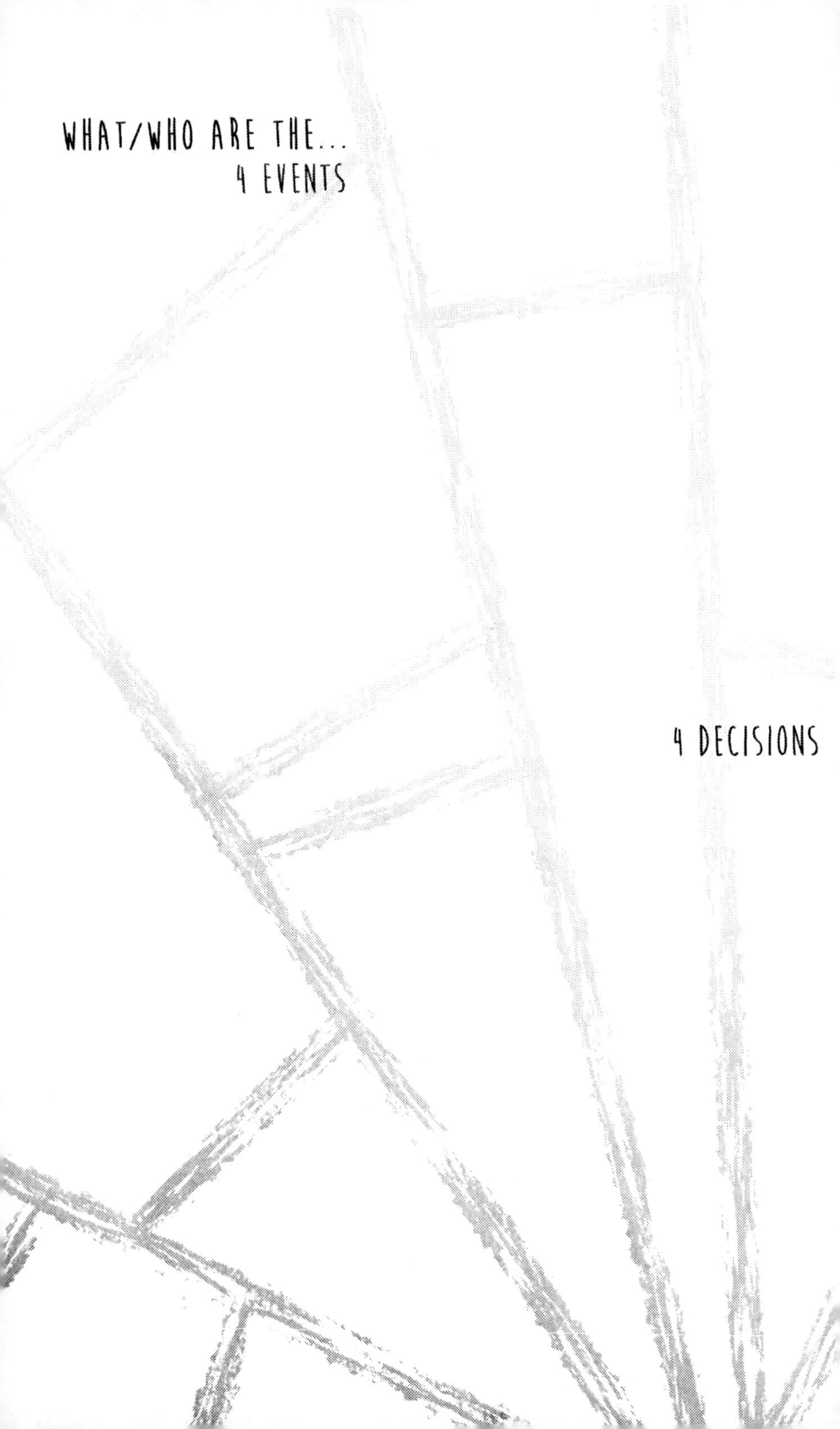

4 DECISIONS

...THAT HAVE MOST SHAPED MY LIFE AND WHO I AM?

IF I WERE TO WRITE THE STORY OF MY LIFE UP TO THIS POINT WHAT WOULD IT SAY?

WRITE YOUR STORY HERE

HAVE I MADE
CONSCIOUS CHOICES
AND DECISIONS
IN MY LIFE SO FAR?
OR HAS LIFE JUST HAPPENED?

AM I MAKING CONSCIOUS
CHOICES TODAY?

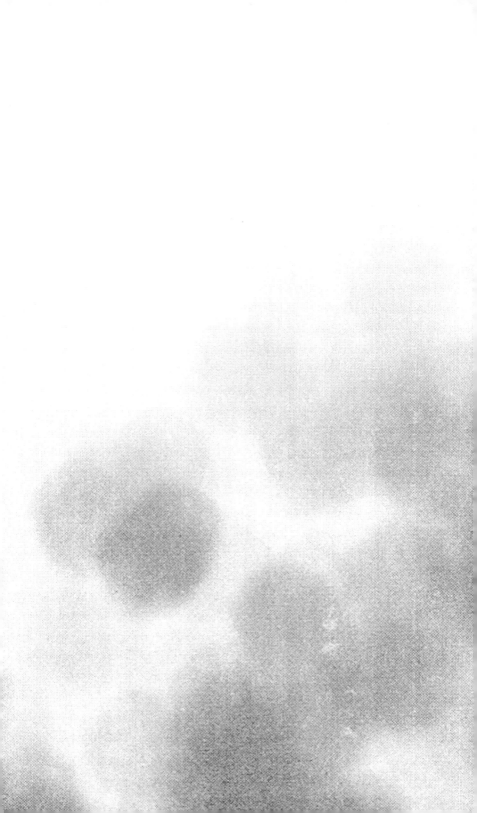

MAKE ONE DECISION
ABOUT SOMETHING
YOU WILL DO
DIFFERENTLY
IN YOUR LIFE
STARTING TODAY

AM I CONSCIOUSLY AWARE
OF HOW MY ACTIONS AND
WORDS IMPACT OTHERS AND
THE WORLD AROUND ME?

Tell someone that you

forgive him/her

FILL THIS PAGE WITH IDEAS, THOUGHTS, QUESTIONS, DRAWINGS...

WHAT KINDS OF BOOKS,
MAGAZINES, WEBSITES,
BLOGS, AND VIDEOS AM I
CHOOSING TO READ AND
WATCH?
LIST THEM HERE:

WHAT VALUE DO THEY ADD
TO MY BEING AND LIFE?

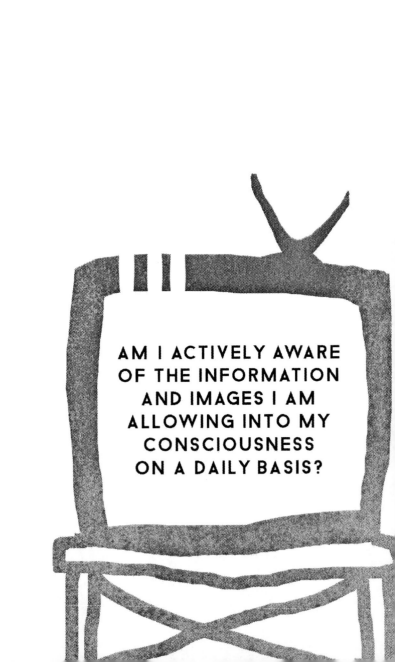

AM I ACTIVELY AWARE
OF THE INFORMATION
AND IMAGES I AM
ALLOWING INTO MY
CONSCIOUSNESS
ON A DAILY BASIS?

CALL OR EMAIL SOMEONE THAT YOU HAVE BEEN
THINKING ABOUT CONTACTING FOR SOME TIME

DO I BELIEVE THAT

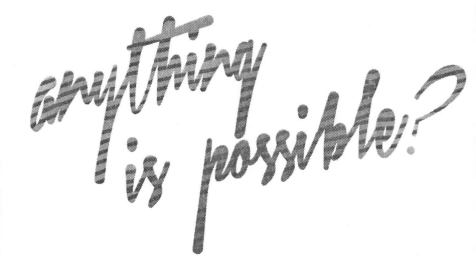

anything is possible?

Do I believe that the energy I take in and put out into the world affects what happens in my life?
How?

GO BACK THROUGH

YOUR CLOSET,
SHELVES,

AND DRAWERS.

CLEAN THEM OUT.

GIVE SOME STUFF AWAY.

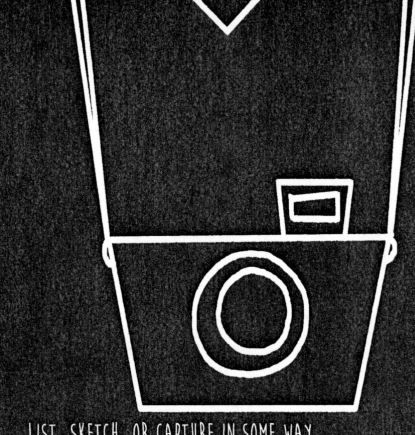

LIST, SKETCH, OR CAPTURE IN SOME WAY
THE SIGHTS, SOUNDS, SMELLS, TASTES YOU
ARE FLOODED WITH FROM THE MOMENT YOU
WAKE UP UNTIL YOU GO TO BED TODAY.

ARE THESE CONTRIBUTING
POSITIVELY AND PRODUCTIVELY TO MY
LIFE? SHOULD I CHOOSE TO EXPOSE
MYSELF IN DIFFERENT WAYS (MORE OR
LESS) TO THESE STIMULI?

MAKE A LIST OF BOOKS, MAGAZINES, WEBSITES, BLOGS, AND VIDEOS THAT YOU WILL READ OR WATCH.

FIND INSPIRATION AND EXPOSE YOURSELF TO A WIDER VARIETY OF SUBJECTS, THOUGHTS, AND VIEWPOINTS.

Am I listening to my body and paying attention to the signs that it gives me?

when I feel tired, energized, or have a distinct feeling in my chest or stomach, what is my body telling me?

TAKE AN INVENTORY OF WHAT YOU ATE THIS PAST WEEK. WRITE YOUR MEALS HERE. BREAKFAST. LUNCH. DINNER. SNACKING.

GO TO YOUR REFRIGERATOR
AND PANTRY. PICK UP YOUR
FAVORITE FOODS. COOKIES.
CHIPS. SNACKS.

READ THE LIST OF
INGREDIENTS
AND LIST THEM HERE.

RESEARCH AND RECORD
THE DESCRIPTION OF
EACH INGREDIENT.

GIVE SOME THOUGHT TO THE
ORIGINS OF YOUR FOOD.
WHERE DOES IT COME FROM?
HOW DID IT GET TO
YOUR PLATE?

COULD I BE EATING DIFFERENTLY?

WHO HAVE I LOVED
IN MY LIFE?
WHO DO I LOVE?

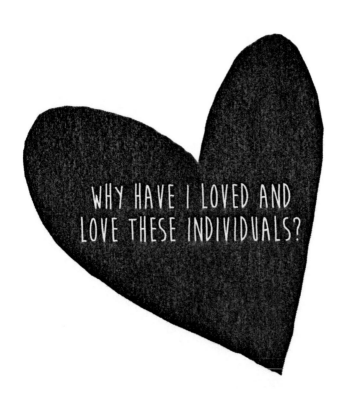

WHY HAVE I LOVED AND
LOVE THESE INDIVIDUALS?

tell someone that you LOVE and APPRECIATE him or her

HOW DO I FEEL ABOUT MY PARENTS? IS THERE ANYTHING THAT I WANT TO TELL MY MOTHER OR FATHER?

What beliefs have I adopted from my parents? Do these beliefs represent who I truly am and want to be?

DO I KNOW THE PEOPLE
IN MY NEIGHBORHOOD
AND COMMUNITY?

LIST 5 PEOPLE YOU KNOW OR HAVE MET IN YOUR NEIGHBORHOOD OR COMMUNITY (A FRIEND, YOUR DENTIST, MAILMAN, THE DELI GUY).

ENGAGE THEM IN A FACE-TO-FACE CONVERSATION. FIND OUT THEIR STORY.

GO TO A COFFEE SHOP OR
RESTAURANT BY YOURSELF,
WITHOUT YOUR PHONE OR
ANY BOOKS.
JUST SIT AND OBSERVE THE
PEOPLE, SIGHTS, AND SOUNDS
AROUND YOU....

WHEN YOU GET BACK HOME, WRITE
ABOUT WHAT YOU OBSERVED AND

DO I BUILD COMMUNITY?

HOW?

AT SCHOOL, I...

AT WORK, I...

IN MY NEIGHBORHOOD, I...

SIMPLE THINGS I CAN START DOING
TO ENCOURAGE COMMUNITY:

I am inspired by...

Fill this page with words, images, thoughts, quotes, drawings that inspire you.

CHOOSE ANY QUESTION THAT IS IMPORTANT TO YOU - SERIOUS
OR JUST PLAIN FUN. NO MATTER HOW SMALL OR TRIVIAL IT
MAY SEEM, IT MIGHT LEAD TO AN IMPORTANT INSIGHT ABOUT
YOU.

EXPLORE IT HERE.

WHY...

DO I LOVE VAMPIRES?

HAVE I NOT FOUND A PARTNER IN MY LIFE YET?

DO I DREAM OF LIVING IN BARCELONA?

DO I FEEL ANGER WHEN I AM AROUND _____?

DO I FEEL STUCK IN MY LIFE?

DO I STILL GET SO EXCITED WHEN I GO TO DISNEY?

DO I HAVE TROUBLE BEING AWAY FROM MY IPHONE?

AM I CONSTANTLY THINKING ABOUT _____?

DO I FEEL MOVED BY THE COLOR RED?

DO I CONTINUE TO REPEAT THE SAME PATTERNS IN MY LIFE?

DO I LOVE THE CIRCUS?

DO I LOVE FOREIGN MOVIES?

WHAT DOES THIS LOVE REPRESENT FOR ME?

WHEN AM I FINALLY GOING TO ASK HER/HIM OUT?

WHERE DO I DREAM OF TRAVELING TO?

WHAT AM I WAITING FOR?

I AM THANKFUL AND
GRATEFUL FOR...

I am interested in and intrigued by....
List places you can visit or volunteer that will help you
further explore your interests and curiosities.

LOOK AT A GLOBE OR
MAP OF THE WORLD.
PICK ONE COUNTRY,
ISLAND, OR BODY
OF WATER THAT
INTERESTS YOU.

GO TO YOUR LOCAL
LIBRARY AND FIND
BOOKS ABOUT IT.
USE THIS SPACE TO
RECORD THE DETAILS
AND INFORMATION
THAT MOST SPOKE
TO YOU....

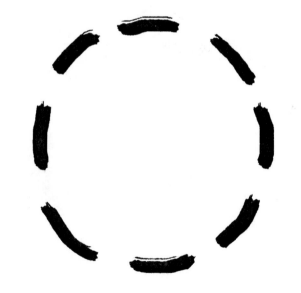

WHAT ARE MY THOUGHTS ABOUT
THE WORLD AND EVERYTHING
THAT IS HAPPENING AROUND ME?

What are my beliefs about...

life

people

the world

myself

love

friendship

courage

honor

justice

equality

What are my beliefs about...

poverty

the Earth

lying

animals

death

reincarnation

joy

passion

a higher being

human consciousness

What is important to me?

What do I feel strongly about?

AM i TELLiNG MYSELF THE TRUTH?
ABOUT MYSELF? MY FEELiNGS?
ABOUT OTHERS? ABOUT MY LiFE?

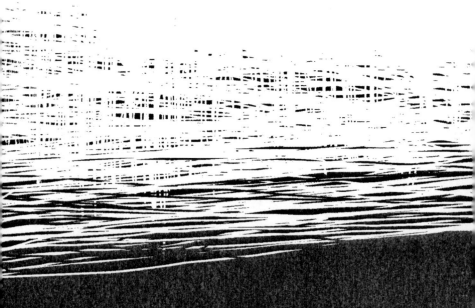

LiST THE LiES YOU HAVE TOLD AND TELL YOURSELF

DO MY BEHAVIORS AND CHOICES REFLECT WHO I TRULY AM AND WHAT I BELIEVE?

OR AM I FOLLOWING SOCIAL RULES AND DOING WHAT OTHERS EXPECT OF ME?·

MAKE A LIST OF EVERYTHING YOU DO BECAUSE YOU THINK YOU SHOULD:

I SHOULD...

DO I REALLY WANT TO DO THIS? IF NOT, WHAT DO I WANT TO DO INSTEAD?

Do I have *toxic* *people* in my life?

Why do I allow them to stay in my life?

ARE MY FAMILY, FRIENDS, RELATIONSHIPS, AND
THE OTHER PEOPLE IN MY LIFE CONTRIBUTING
POSITIVELY TO MY WELL-BEING?

IF NOT, WHAT CAN I CHANGE?

DRAW OR PLACE IMAGES ON THIS PAGE THAT
MAKE YOU FEEL PEACEFUL. USE MANY COLORS.

VOLUNTEER AT A SOUP
KITCHEN, ANIMAL
SHELTER, HOSPITAL,
CHILD CARE CENTER,
OR ANY PLACE IN NEED
OF HELP.

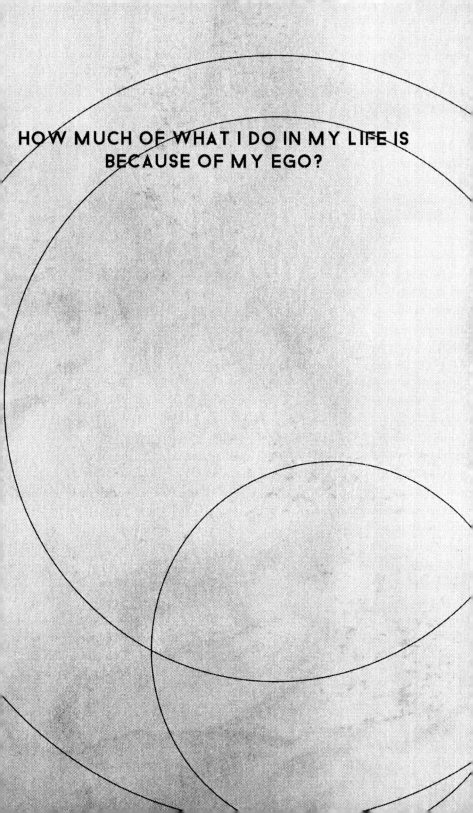

HOW MUCH OF WHAT I DO IN MY LIFE IS
BECAUSE OF MY EGO?

WHEN I WALK INTO A ROOM, WHAT DO PEOPLE FIRST NOTICE ABOUT ME?

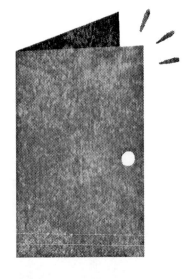

HOW OFTEN DO I VOICE WHAT I TRULY THINK AND FEEL?

MAKE A LIST OF THE TIMES WHEN YOU HAVE PUT ON A
SHOW AND BEEN FAKE TO YOURSELF AND OTHERS.

AM I LIVING AS MY
TRUE AUTHENTIC SELF?

THE ME I AM WHEN I AM ALON

THE ME THAT I SHOW TO OTHERS

IS THERE A GAP?

WHY IS THERE A DIFFERENCE?

AM I LISTENING TO MY INTUITION?
DO I HEAR MY INNER VOICE?
WHAT DOES IT SAY?

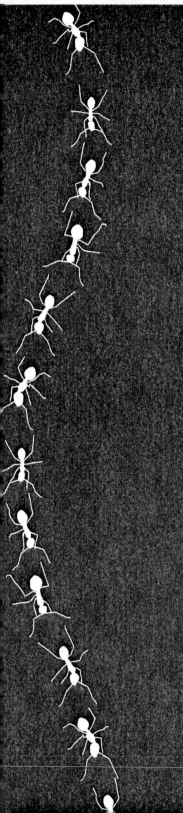

FIND AN ANIMAL-

YOUR PET DOG//CAT//FISH,

A LIZARD, A BIRD, A SQUIRREL.

SPEND SOME TIME OBSERVING ITS BEHAVIOR

AND ENERGY...

AM I PAYING ATTENTION TO THE WORLD
AND ENERGY AROUND ME?

PICK ANOTHER QUESTION THAT YOU WANT TO EXPLORE.

EXPLORE IT HERE

WHAT DO I VALUE MOST IN LIFE?

I WANT TO USE THE GIFT THAT IS
MY LIFE TO...

THE MISSION OF MY LIFE AND SOUL IS:

SOME LIFE AND SOUL MISSIONS:

RESPECT AND PROTECT THE PLANE

HAVE ADVENTURES AND EXPERIENCE THE WORLD

CREATE OPPORTUNITIES FOR OTHERS

LIVE A NATURAL, SIMPLE LIFE

FIGHT THE UNFAIR TREATMENT OF OTHERS

PROTECT ENDANGERED WILDLIFE

BE AUTHENTIC

BE FREE

BE HEALTHY

UNLOCK THE INCREDIBLE POTENTIAL IN OTHERS

CONTINUOUSLY EVOLVE

LIVE AND SHARE THE MAGIC OF LIFE

LOVE AND BE LOVED

HELP TO SAVE THE EVERGLADES

BRING INSPIRATION TO YOUNG PEOPLE

HELP OTHERS TO GROW AND LEARN

BE A POSITIVE LIGHT

BE JOYFUL

CURE
CANCER

Make a list of what is
most important to you

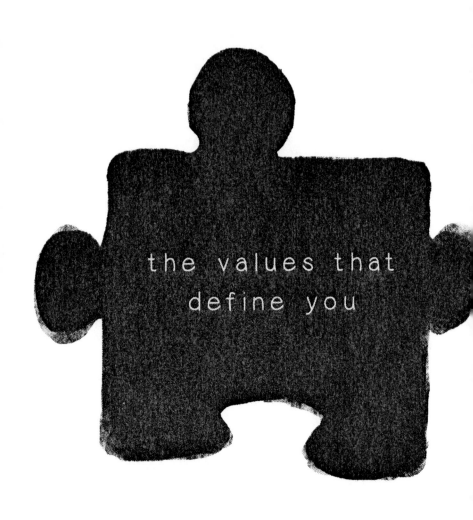

the values that
define you

Circle the top 7-10 that you
cannot live without.

These are your core values.

EXAMPLES OF VALUES:
Love - Peace of mind - Telling the
truth - Wealth - Learning - Being
challenged - Being inspired -
Working hard - Playing hard -
Making an impact on the world -
Fairness - Loyalty - Being healthy

what do I want most in life?
what are my dreams?

DESCRIBE YOUR LIFE AS YOU WOULD LIKE IT TO BE 10 YEARS FROM NOW...

WHAT ARE YOU DOING, SEEING, AND FEELING?

WHAT DOES IT FEEL LIKE TO BE YOUR TRUE AUTHENTIC SELF?

WHERE ARE YOU LIVING?

WHERE DO YOU WORK? HOW ARE YOU SPENDING YOUR TIME?

WITH WHOM DO YOU SHARE YOUR LIFE AND EXPERIENCES?

DESCRIBE YOUR LIFE
AS YOU WOULD
LIKE IT TO BE

20

YEARS FROM NOW...

DESCRIBE YOUR LIFE
AS YOU WOULD
LIKE IT TO BE
WHEN YOU ARE

80

YEARS OLD...

78

71

84

82

83

87 88

86

90

IF I LIVE TO BE
100 YEARS OLD,
WHAT WOULD MY
LIFE HAVE BEEN
LIKE IF I LIVED
IT EXACTLY AS I
WANT TO LIVE IT?

91

96

94

95

98 99 100

WRITE ONE OR TWO OF YOUR FAVORITE QUOTES ON THIS PAGE.

Describe why you love this quote and what it says about you.

Here is one of our

DREAM AS IF YOU'LL LIVE
FOREVER. LIVE AS IF
YOU'LL DIE TOMORROW.
- *JAMES DEAN*

WHAT OR WHO AM I ALLOWING TO HOLD ME BACK IN MY LIFE?

WHAT AM I AFRAID OF?

IF I WAS NOT AFRAID, WHAT WOULD I BE DOING DIFFERENTLY?

WHAT
    HAVE I

BEEN

    PUTTING
OFF DOING?

WHAT WOULD I LOVE
TO BE SPENDING MORE
    TIME ON?

DO I SEE ANY OTHER PATTERNS?
ARE MY PATTERNS POSITIVE?
DO I NEED TO CHANGE ANY OF
MY LIFE PATTERNS?

GO BACK TO YOUR LIFE STORY AND
MOST IMPORTANT MOMENTS / TURNING POINTS
IN YOUR LIFE MAP

ARE THERE PATTERNS AND
THEMES OVER THE YEARS IN MY:

ACTIONS/CHOICES/DECISIONS

RELATIONSHIPS

CAREER SUCCESS, FAILURES,
CHALLENGES

FEELINGS - MOMENTS WHEN I HAVE
FELT GREAT JOY, SADNESS, PASSION,
PEACE, ETC.

DO I TRUST MYSELF?
DO I LOVE MYSELF?

AM I BURDENED BY
AND HANGING ON TO MY PAST?
IS THERE SOMETHING I NEED TO FINALLY
ACCEPT OR JUST LET GO OF?

Go back to the pages where you answered the questions 'what makes me uniquely me?', 'what are my skills and my characteristics?', 'My good and bad habits?'

Does the life and career that you dream of creating in 10, 20, and 50 years from now match and make the most of your unique passions, qualities, skills, and characteristics?

Go back to your core values...

Do my actions match my values?

Do my life and career dreams
match and support my values and
what is most important to me?

I WANT THE PURPOSE OF MY LIFE TO BE...

HOW AM I SPENDING MY TIME?
DRAW OUT YOUR WEEKDAYS AND
HOW YOU SPEND YOUR TIME:

M

T

W

TH

F

DRAW OUT YOUR WEEKENDS

WHAT ARE THE DIFFERENT AREAS OF MY LIFE?

FRIENDS. FAMILY. RELATIONSHIPS. SCHOOL. HEALTH. WORK. NETFLIX. HOBBIES. SOCIAL MEDIA. OTHERS?

AREAS OF MY LIFE: TIME I SPEND ON THIS AREA:

AM I SPENDING TOO MUCH OR TOO LITTLE TIME ON WHAT IS MOST IMPORTANT TO ME?

ARE MY TIME AND ENERGY SPENT IN A WAY THAT MAKES ME FEEL

HAPPY?

YES ☐
NO ☐

FULFILLED?

☐ YES
☐ NO

WHY OR WHY NOT?

health

relationships

work

hobbies

Do I keep the different areas of my life separate from each other?

Are there areas of my life that I could integrate more?

Hobbies...Work

Health...Relationships

Relationships...Hobbies

Work...Social Media

How?

HOW COULD I BE SPENDING MY TIME DIFFERENTLY
TODAY SO I CAN ENJOY THE MOMENT AS WELL AS BE
MOVING TOWARDS MY LIFE AND CAREER DREAMS?

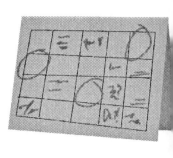

CAN I ELIMINATE SOME COMMITMENTS THAT ARE NOT
ESSENTIAL? CAN I SAY 'NO' MORE OFTEN?

DO WHATEVER YOU WANT
WITH THIS PAGE...

WHO ARE THE PEOPLE WHO CAN SUPPORT
AND INSPIRE ME ON MY LIFE JOURNEY?

What seeds can I be planting
today to start exploring and
cultivating my dreams?

EXAMPLES OF SEEDS WE CAN PLANT

Meet at least one new person every week.

Volunteer somewhere where you will meet interesting people who are doing the work you want to do.

Invite someone interesting for coffee or tea.

Take a new class or workshop related to your passion.

Ask someone you respect for feedback on your work.

Create your dream project and ask someone you find inspirational to collaborate with you on it.

Find someone on LinkedIn or FB who works at one of your dream companies, connect with him or her.

Send him or her a message.

Sign a petition.

Open a new bank account to start saving money for a new project.

Research cities you dream of living in.

Visit one of the people you connected with on LinkedIn and ask them to give you a tour of their company.

Walk a mile - today.

Plan a trip to a city where you would love to live in the future.

Create a website or portfolio to showcase you and your work.

Start writing.

Walk to work instead of drive.

Find a mentor.

Take a free class on Coursera.

List or draw the seeds
that you will plant starting today

Go back to your core values and your description of the overall life you envision for yourself:
List the type of jobs and careers that will help you to create this life.

Who can help me move towards living my dreams?

NAME: HOW CAN THIS PERSON HELP ME?

What stories do I want to tell about myself and my life?

about my time in high school?

about my time in college?

about my relationships?

about my career?

about my life?

How do I want the story of my life to continue from this moment forward?

what story do I want to tell about what will
happen this year in my life?
write the story here.

I will start to make these stories

become a reality today by...

COVER THIS PAGE COMPLETELY WITH COLOR

COMMIT TO A DAILY RITUAL THAT WILL HELP
YOU TO GROW YOUR AWARENESS, LISTEN
WITH YOUR HEART, AND STAY CONNECTED TO
YOURSELF.

I COMMIT TO:

EXAMPLES OF DAILY RITUALS:

PREPARE AND DRINK A CUP OF
GREEN TEA IN COMPLETE SILENCE

LISTEN TO A SONG

WRITE IN YOUR JOURNAL

SIT OUTSIDE FOR 20 MINUTES

TURN OFF YOUR COMPUTER
AND DEVICES BY
8PM EVERY NIGHT

SIT WITH YOUR EYES CLOSED,
KEEPING YOUR MIND CLEAR

DO A DANCE

GO FOR A WALK

TALK TO MY MOM, SISTER, OR
BEST FRIEND FOR 10 MINUTES

GO TO SLEEP BY 10PM

BREATHE DEEPLY FOR 50 COUNTS

PUT SOME COLORFUL PAINT ON YOUR
BLANK CANVAS

EAT A HEALTHY MEAL EVERY DAY

LISTEN TO THE BIRDS SINGING

Go back through the pages of your journal.

Take the time to read your thoughts and what you have written.

What did you learn about yourself?

What insights did you gain about yourself and your life?

Write them down here.

WHAT QUESTIONS AM I STILL LEFT WITH
ABOUT MYSELF AND MY LIFE?

What will I do differently when
I wake up tomorrow?

http://www.project-be.com/